Contents

Math Centers K-1

What's Great About This Book

Centers are a wonderful, fun way for students to practice important skills. The 12 centers in this book are self-contained and portable. Students may work at a table or even on the floor. Once you've made the centers, they're ready to use at any time.

Everything You Need

- Teacher direction page
- Preparing the center
- Using the center
- Self-checking key
- Full-color materials needed for the center
- Reproducible record forms

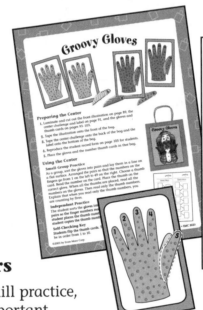

How to Use the Centers

The centers are intended for skill practice, not to introduce skills. It is important to model the use of each center before students do the "Independent Practice" task.

Two options are given for using each center:

1. **Small-Group Practice**—this option provides directions for introducing the center to students.

2. **Independent Practice**—the center task card provides directions for independent use.

Questions to Consider

- Will students select a center, or will you assign one?
- Will there be a specific block of time for centers, or will the centers be used throughout the day?
- Where will you place the centers for easy access by students?
- What procedure will students use when they need help with the center tasks?
- Where will students store completed work?
- How will you track the tasks and centers completed by each student?

Making a Bag Center

Materials

- medium-size gift bag with handles
- scissors
- double-stick tape
- self-closing plastic bags

Steps to Follow

1. Laminate and cut out the bag front illustration, the center task, center manipulatives, and the center label.

2. Reproduce the student record form.

3. Tape the illustration onto the front of the gift bag. Tape the center task labels onto the back.

4. Tape the center label to the bottom of the bag. The label will be visible when the bag is folded for storage.

5. Place manipulatives and record forms in the bag.

My Bug Jar

Preparing the Center

1. Laminate and cut out the front illustration on page 5, the center challenge and label on page 7, and the bug jar sorting mats and bugs on pages 9–17.

2. Tape the illustration onto the front of the bag.

3. Tape the center challenge onto the back of the bag and the label onto the bottom of the bag.

4. Reproduce the student record form on page 19 for students.

5. Place the bug jar sorting mats and bugs in the bag.

Using the Center

Small-Group Practice

Each student has a bug jar sorting mat. The bug cards remain in the bag. Students take turns reaching into the bag and removing a handful of bugs. They sort the bugs, count how many of each kind they have, and then record the numbers on the record form. Finally, they write an equation to tell how many bugs each student has in all.

Independent Practice

The student chooses a handful of bugs and sorts them by bug type. The student counts the number of each type and records the information on the record form. The student writes an equation to tell how many bugs there are in all.

Self-Checking Key

Students flip sorted bug cards to see if the colors are the same. They may also recount all the cards before returning them to the bag to make sure that they have the correct sums for their equations.

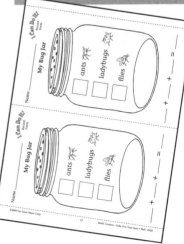

My Bug Jar

Math Centers—Take It to Your Seat • EMC 3020

Hopping Away

Hopping Away

Skills:
Counting, Subtraction

Hopping Away

1. Place some frogs on a lily pad.

2. Count the frogs. Write the number.

3. Decide how many frogs will hop away. Write the number.

4. Make the frogs hop away.

5. Count the frogs that are left. Write the number.

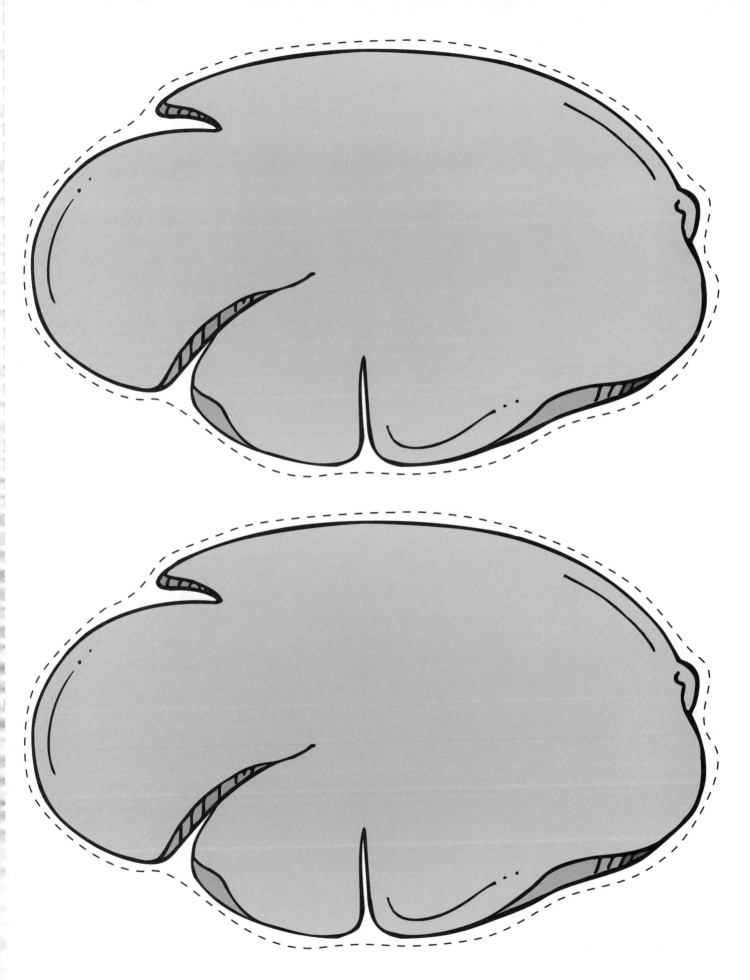

Animal Count

©2003 by Evan-Moor Corp.   40   Math Centers—Take It to Your Seat • EMC 3020

Animal Count

Skill:
Counting

Animal Count

1. Choose an animal.

2. Count the eyes on the animal.

3. Record the number of eyes on the record form.

4. Repeat for each of the animal features on the record form.

5. Check to see if you counted correctly.

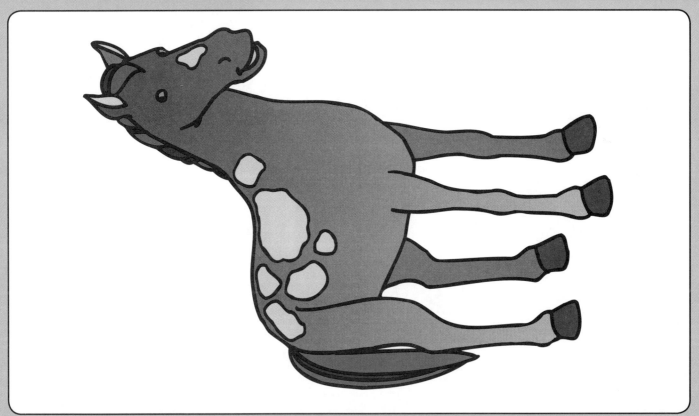

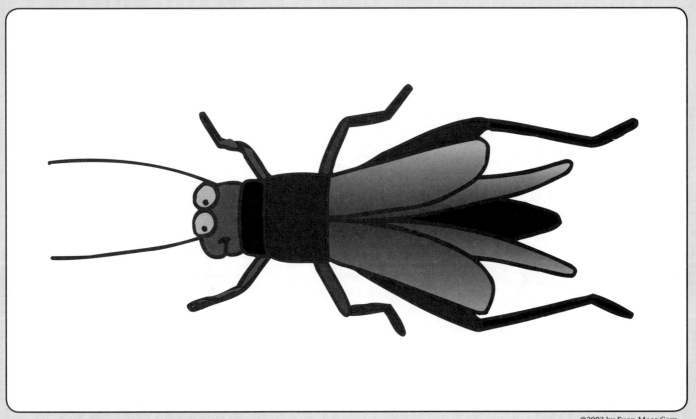

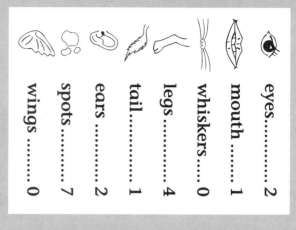

eyes............2
mouth........1
whiskers.....0
legs............4
tail..............1
ears............2
spots.........7
wings.........0

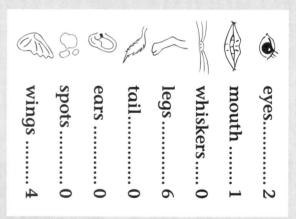

eyes............2
mouth........1
whiskers.....0
legs............6
tail..............0
ears............0
spots.........0
wings.........4

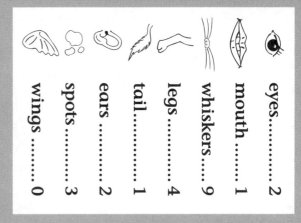

eyes.........2
mouth........1
whiskers.....9
legs..........4
tail............1
ears..........2
spots..........3
wings 0

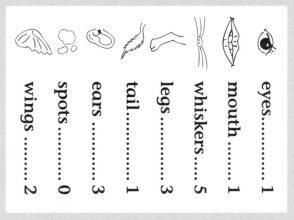

eyes.........1
mouth........1
whiskers.....5
legs..........3
tail............1
ears..........3
spots..........0
wings 2

Math Centers—Take It to Your Seat • EMC 3020

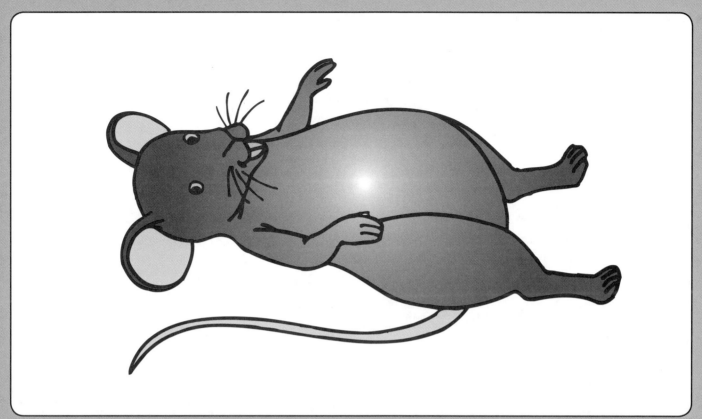

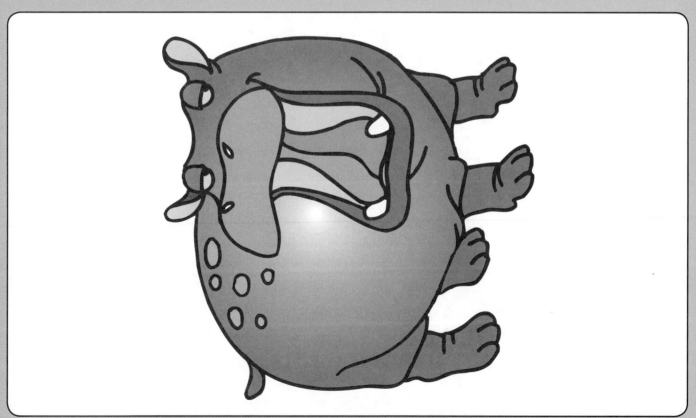

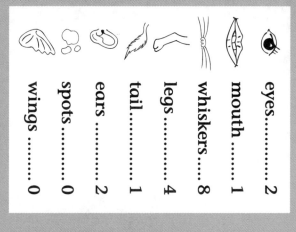

eyes.............2
mouth.........1
whiskers.....8
legs...............4
tail................1
ears..............2
spots............0
wings...........0

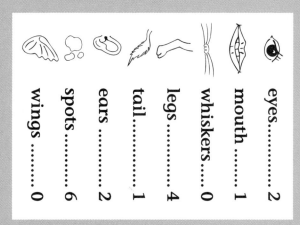

eyes.............2
mouth.........1
whiskers.....0
legs...............4
tail................1
ears..............2
spots............6
wings...........0

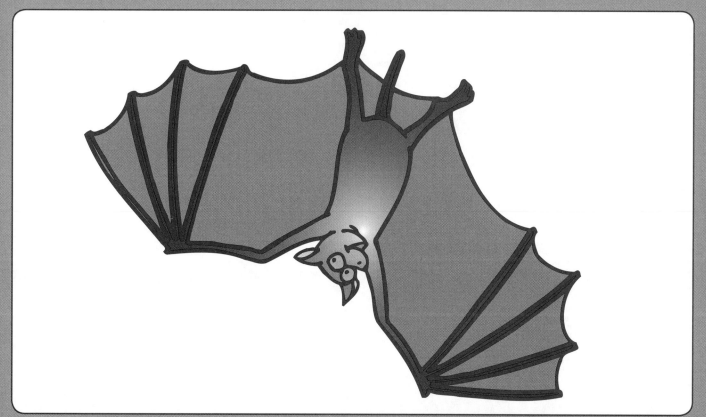

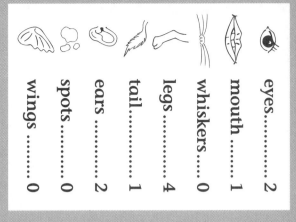

eyes 2
mouth 1
whiskers 0
tail 1
legs 4
ears 2
spots 0
wings 0

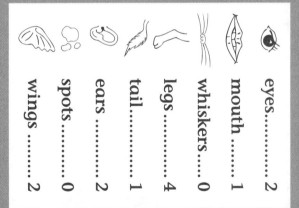

eyes 2
mouth 1
whiskers 0
tail 1
legs 4
ears 2
spots 0
wings 2

Name _____

Animal Count

Circle the animal.

horse   cricket   dog   wildthing

mouse   hippo   monkey   bat

Write the number.

 eyes   tail

 mouth   ears

 whiskers   spots

 legs   wings

Name _____

Animal Count

Circle the animal.

horse   cricket   dog   wildthing

mouse   hippo   monkey   bat

Write the number.

 eyes   tail

 mouth   ears

 whiskers   spots

 legs   wings

Puzzle a Hundred

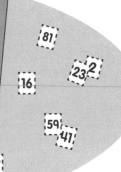

Preparing the Center

1. Laminate and cut out the front illustration on page 53, the center challenge and label on page 55, and the number puzzle mats and number cards on pages 57–67.

2. Tape the illustration onto the front of the bag.

3. Tape the center challenge onto the back of the bag and the label onto the bottom of the bag.

4. Reproduce the student record form on page 69 for students.

5. Place the number mats and the number cards in the bag.

Using the Center

Small-Group Practice

Each student has a number mat. The number cards remain in the bag. Draw a number card from the bag. Show the number. Students look at their cards and claim the card if it fills a blank on their mat. Repeat. Students try to complete their mats by filling in each blank. Finally, they color in all the numbers that filled the blanks on the record form.

Independent Practice

The student chooses a number mat. The student chooses number cards and checks to see if the cards fill a blank on the mat. When every blank is filled, the student compares the number puzzle to the record form. The student colors in the squares on the record form that were missing.

Self-Checking Key

Students compare their completed number puzzle mats to the numbers on the record form.

Puzzle a Hundred

Math Centers—Take It to Your Seat • EMC 3020

Puzzle a Hundred

16

Skills:
Number Order,
Number Recognition

Puzzle a Hundred

1. Take a number puzzle mat.

2. Choose a number card. Does the number fill a blank in your puzzle?

3. Keep choosing numbers until every blank is filled.

4. Color the numbers on the record form.

5. Check. Do the numbers on the record form match the numbers on your puzzle?

Puzzle a Hundred Mat

1		3	4	5	6	7	8	9	10
11	12	13	14		16	17	18	19	20
21	22	23	24	25	26		28	29	30
31	32		34	35	36	37	38	39	40
41	42	43	44	45	46	47	48	49	
51	52	53		55	56	57	58	59	60
	62	63	64	65	66	67	68	69	70
71	72	73	74	75		77	78	79	80
81	82	83	84	85	86	87	88		90
91	92	93	94	95	96	97		99	100

Puzzle a Hundred Mat

1	2	3	4	5	6		8	9	10
11	12		14	15	16	17	18	19	20
21	22	23	24		26	27	28	29	30
	32	33	34	35	36	37	38	39	40
41	42	43	44	45	46	47		49	50
51	52	53	54	55	56	57	58		60
61	62	63		65	66	67	68	69	70
71	72	73	74	75	76		78	79	80
	82	83	84	85	86	87	88	89	90
91	92	93	94	95	96	97	98	99	

Puzzle a Hundred Mat

1	2	3	4		6	7	8	9	10
11	12	13	14	15	16	17	18	19	
21	22	23		25	26	27	28	29	30
31		33	34	35	36	37	38	39	40
41	42	43	44	45		47	48	49	50
51	52		54	55	56	57	58	59	60
61	62	63	64	65	66		68	69	70
	72	73	74	75	76	77	78	79	80
81	82	83	84	85	86	87		89	90
91	92	93	94	95	96	97	98		100

Math Centers—Take It to Your Seat • EMC 3020

Puzzle a Hundred Mat

1	2		4	5	6	7	8	9	10
11	12	13	14	15	16		18	19	20
21		23	24	25	26	27	28	29	30
31	32	33	34	35		37	38	39	40
41	42	43	44	45	46	47	48		50
	52	53	54	55	56	57	58	59	60
61	62	63	64		66	67	68	69	70
71	72	73		75	76	77	78	79	80
81	82	83	84	85	86	87	88	89	
91	92	93	94	95		97	98	99	100

Puzzle a Hundred Mat

1	2	3	4	5	6	7		9	10
11	12	13	14	15		17	18	19	20
21	22		24	25	26	27	28	29	30
31	32	33	34	35	36	37		39	40
	42	43	44	45	46	47	48	49	50
51	52	53	54	55	56		58	59	60
61	62	63	64	65	66	67	68	69	
71	72	73	74	75	76	77	78		80
81		83	84	85	86	87	88	89	90
91	92	93		95	96	97	98	99	100

Math Centers—Take It to Your Seat • EMC 3020

Number Cards

2	3	5	7	8
13	15	16	17	20
22	23	24	25	27
31	32	33	36	38
41	46	48	49	50
51	53	54	57	59
61	64	65	67	70
71	74	76	77	79
81	82	88	89	90
94	96	98	99	100

Math Centers—Take It to Your Seat • EMC 3020

Math Centers—Take It to Your Seat • EMC 3020

Name _____

Puzzle a Hundred

Circle the number puzzle you finished. ⬚1⬚ ⬚2⬚ ⬚3⬚ ⬚4⬚ ⬚5⬚

Color in the squares to show the numbers that were missing on your puzzle.

1	2	3	4	5	6	7	8	9	10
11	12	13	14	15	16	17	18	19	20
21	22	23	24	25	26	27	28	29	30
31	32	33	34	35	36	37	38	39	40
41	42	43	44	45	46	47	48	49	50
51	52	53	54	55	56	57	58	59	60
61	62	63	64	65	66	67	68	69	70
71	72	73	74	75	76	77	78	79	80
81	82	83	84	85	86	87	88	89	90
91	92	93	94	95	96	97	98	99	100

Pretty Pants

Preparing the Center

1. Laminate and cut out the front illustration on page 71, the center challenge and label on page 73, and the pants and number cards on pages 75–85.

2. Tape the illustration onto the front of the bag.

3. Tape the center challenge onto the back of the bag and the label onto the bottom of the bag.

4. Reproduce the student record form on page 87 for students.

5. Place the pants and the number cards in the bag.

Using the Center

Small-Group Practice

As a group, lay the pairs of pants in a straight line on a flat surface. Lay the number cards in order on the pants to count the legs. Read the numbers aloud. Then read only the red numbers aloud. Explain that each red number represents two legs, so reading the red numbers is counting by twos. Students record the red numbers in order on the record form.

Independent Practice

The student lays the pants in a line on a flat surface. The student places the number cards in order on the legs of the pants from left to right. The student reads the numbers aloud. Then the student reads the red numbers aloud. The student writes the red numbers in order on the record form.

Self-Checking Key

Students take the red numbers off the pants. When they are laid side by side in "counting by twos" order, the student can flip them over and see a, b, c, etc., in order.

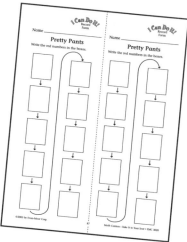

Pretty Pants

71

Math Centers—Take It to Your Seat • EMC 3020

Pretty Pants

Skills:
Number Ordering,
Counting by 1s and 2s

Pretty Pants

1. Lay the pants in a line.

2. Place the number cards in number order on the squares.

3. Read all the numbers aloud.

4. Read only the red numbers aloud.

5. Write the red numbers on the record form.

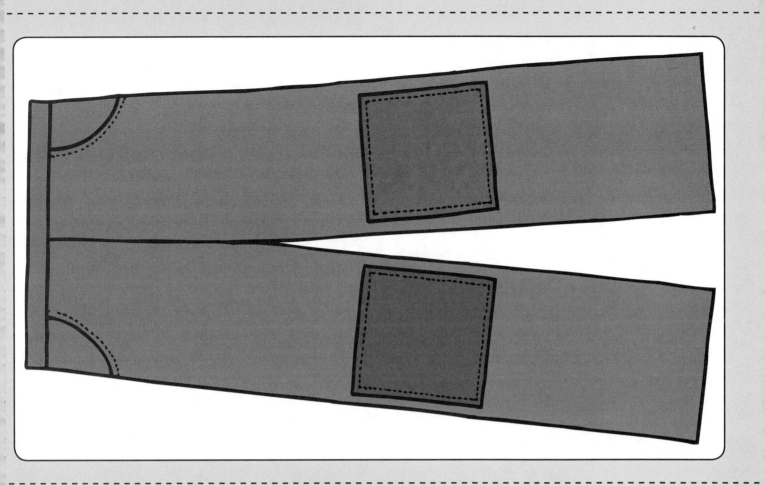

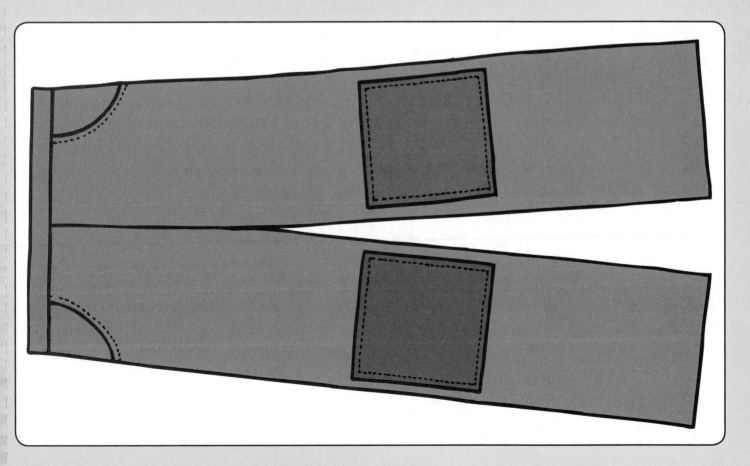

Math Centers—Take It to Your Seat • EMC 3020

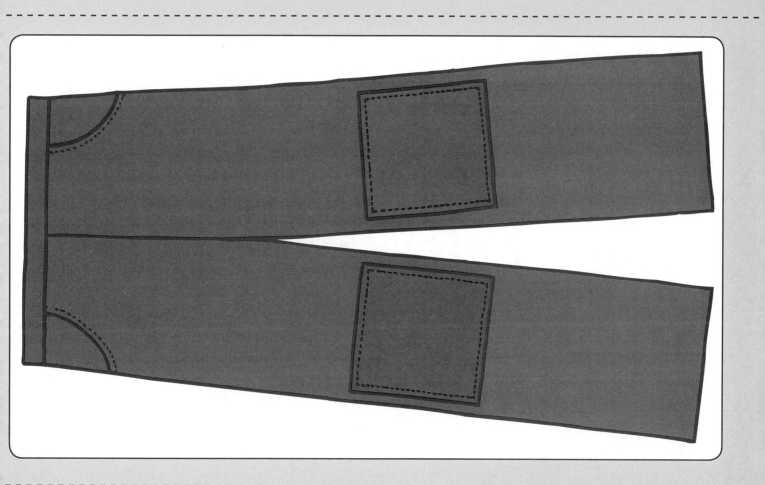

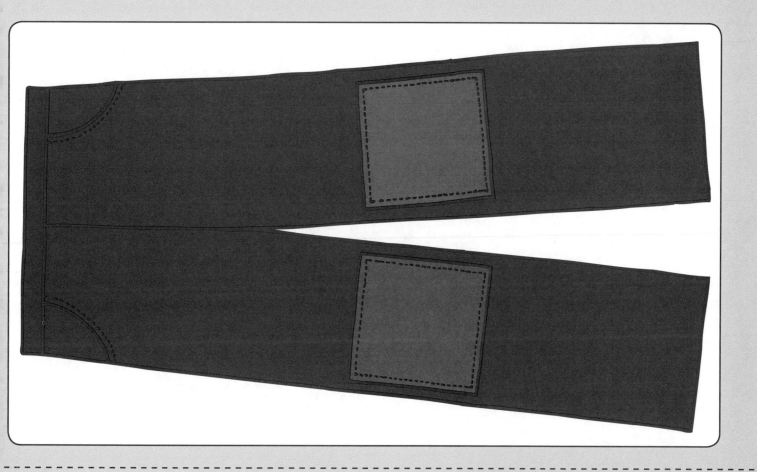

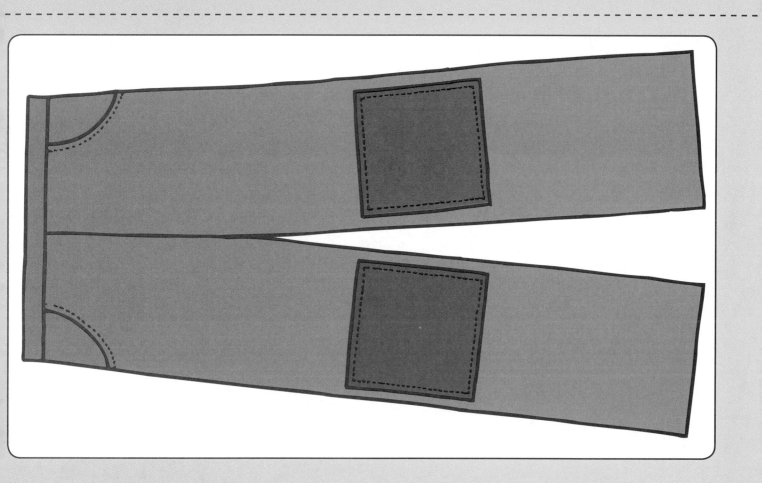

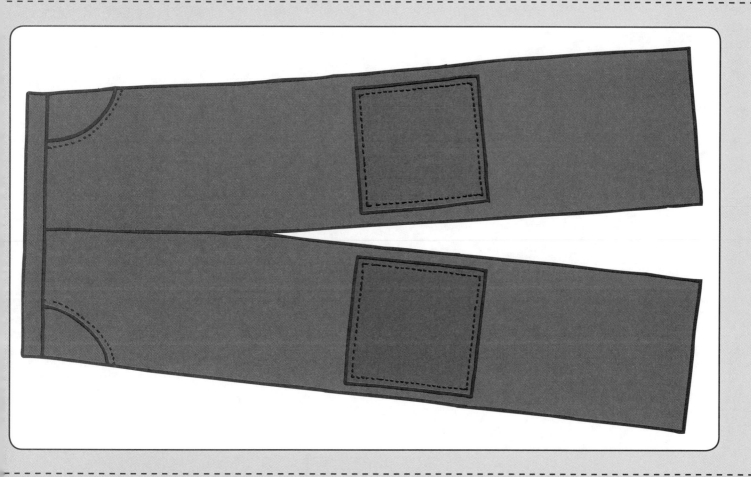

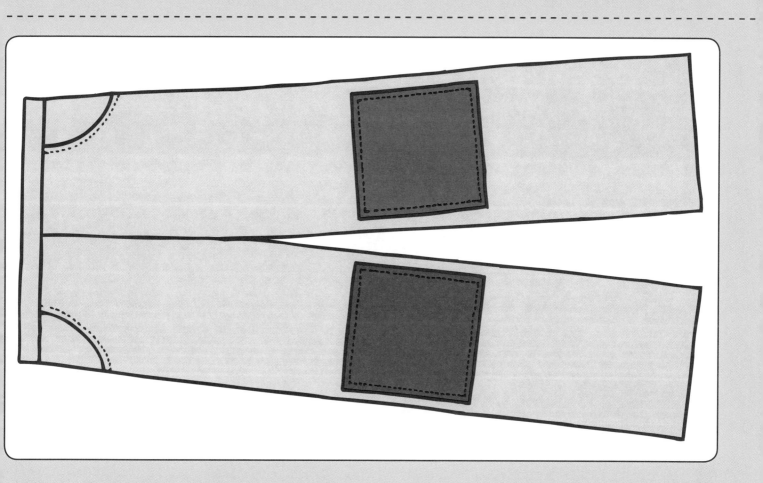

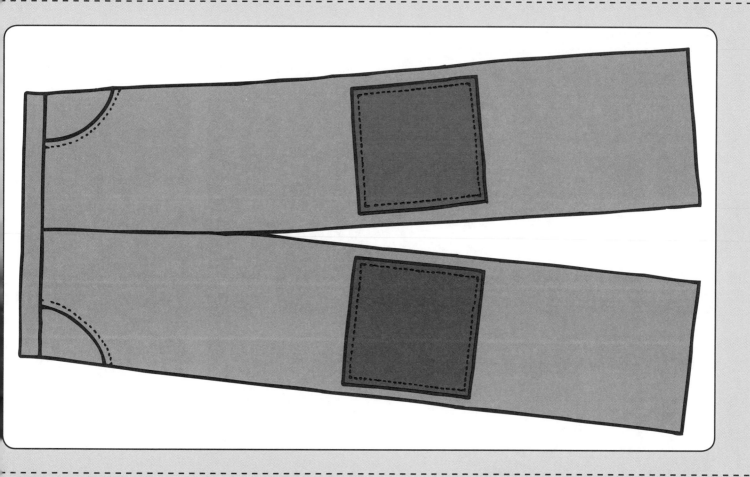

82

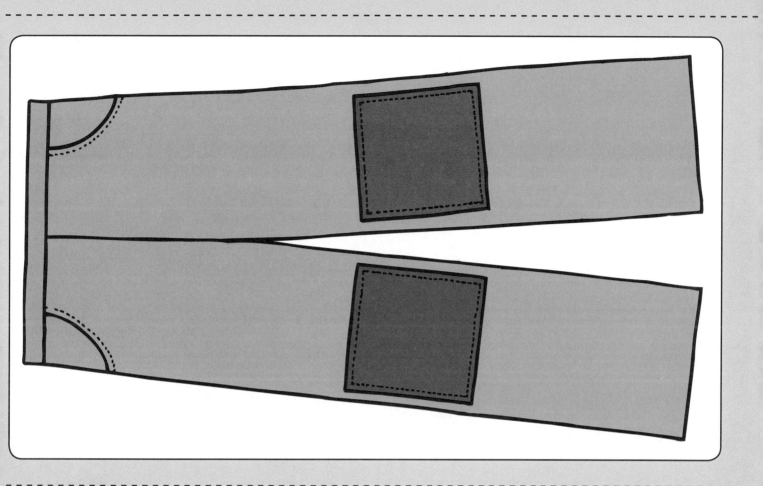

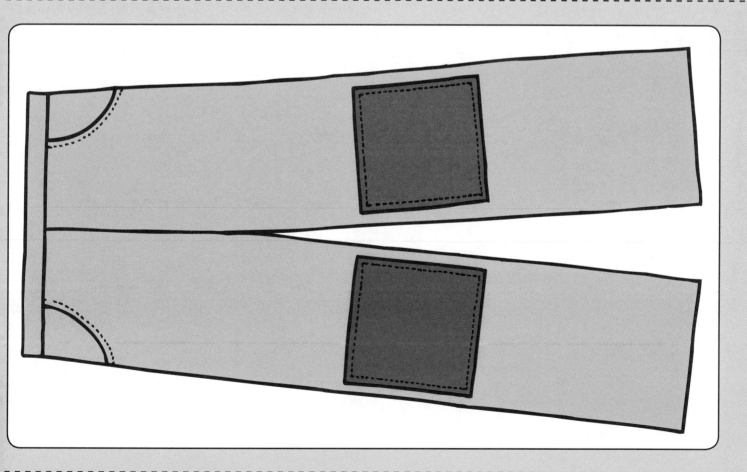

Math Centers—Take It to Your Seat • EMC 3020

Number Cards

1	2	3	4	5
6	7	8	9	10
11	12	13	14	15
16	17	18	19	20

 Math Centers—Take It to Your Seat • EMC 3020

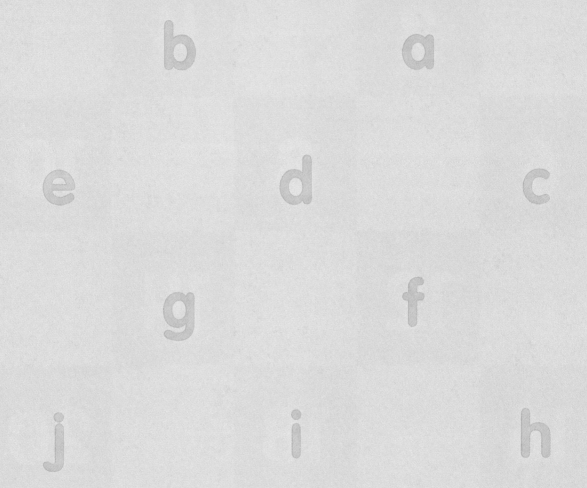

Name _____

Pretty Pants

Write the red numbers in the boxes.

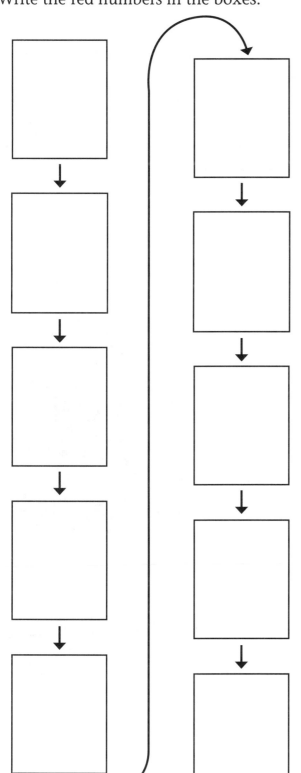

Name _____

Pretty Pants

Write the red numbers in the boxes.

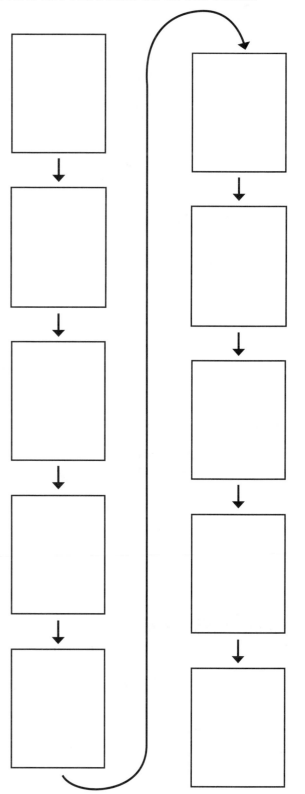

Groovy Gloves

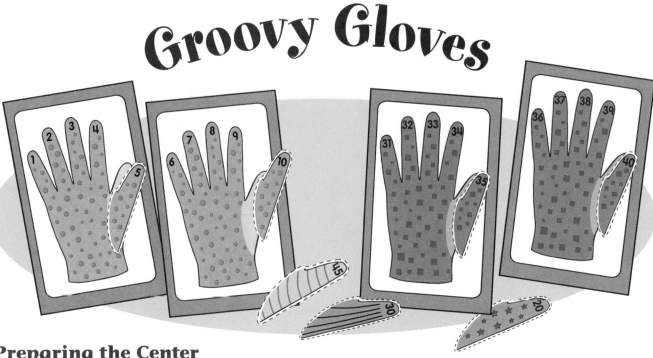

Preparing the Center

1. Laminate and cut out the front illustration on page 89, the center challenge and label on page 91, and the gloves and thumb cards on pages 93–103.

2. Tape the illustration onto the front of the bag.

3. Tape the center challenge onto the back of the bag and the label onto the bottom of the bag.

4. Reproduce the student record form on page 105 for students.

5. Place the gloves and the number thumb cards in the bag.

Using the Center

Small-Group Practice

As a group, sort the gloves into pairs and lay them in a line on a flat surface. Arrange the pairs so that the numbers on the fingers go from 1 on the left to 49 on the right. Choose a thumb card. Read the number on the card. Place the thumb on the correct glove. When all the thumbs are placed, read all the numbers on the gloves. Then read only the thumb numbers. Explain that when you read only the thumb numbers, you are counting by fives.

Independent Practice

The student sorts the gloves into pairs. The student arranges the pairs so the finger numbers read left to right from 1 to 49. The student places the thumb numbers on the correct gloves. The student copies the thumb numbers onto the record form.

Self-Checking Key

Students flip the thumb cards. The numbers on the back should be in order from 1 to 10.

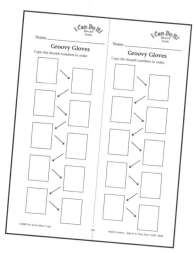

Groovy Gloves

Math Centers—Take It to Your Seat • EMC 3020

Groovy Gloves

Skills:
Sorting, Number Order, Counting by 5s

Groovy Gloves

1. Place the pairs together.

2. Arrange the pairs so the numbers go from 1 to 49.

3. Place the thumbs in the correct places.

4. Read all the numbers.

5. Read just the thumb numbers.

6. Copy the thumb numbers onto the record form.

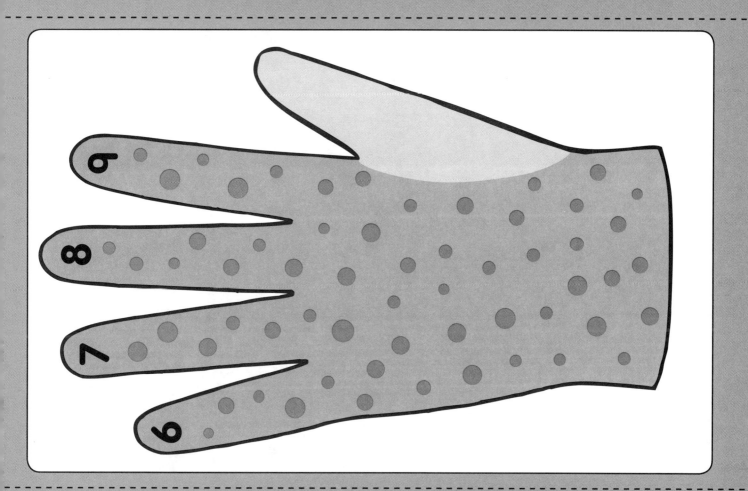

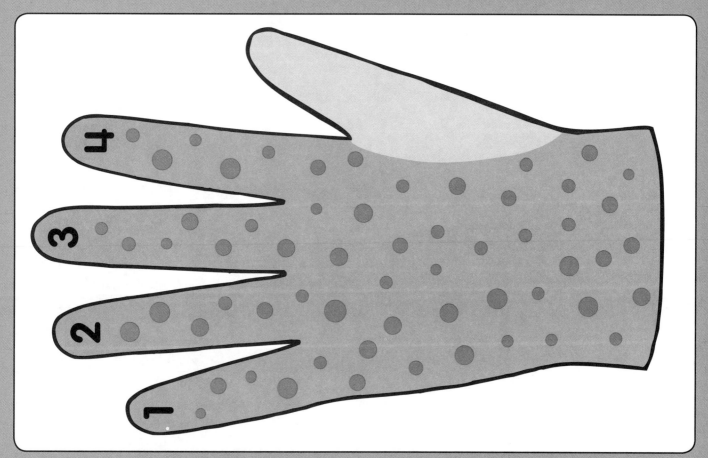

Math Centers—Take It to Your Seat • EMC 3020

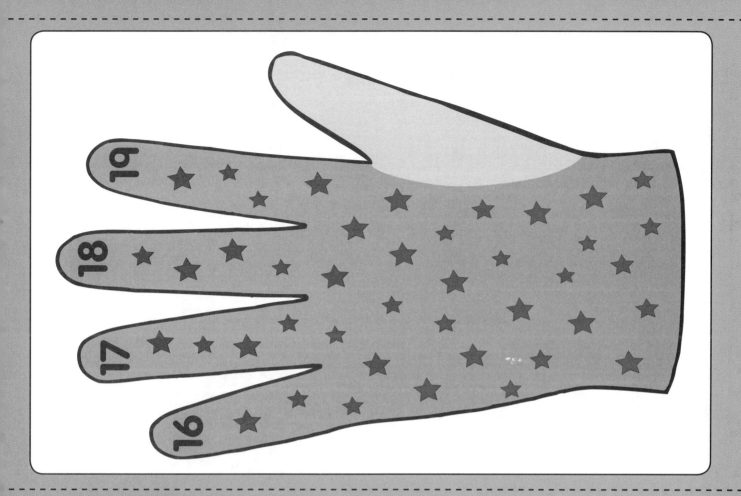

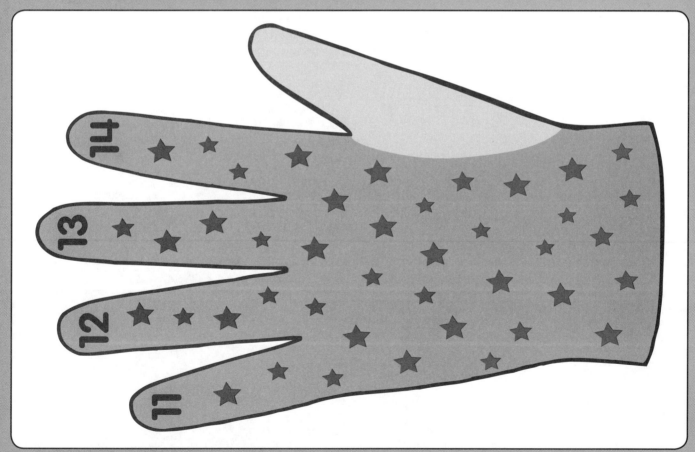

Math Centers—Take It to Your Seat • EMC 3020

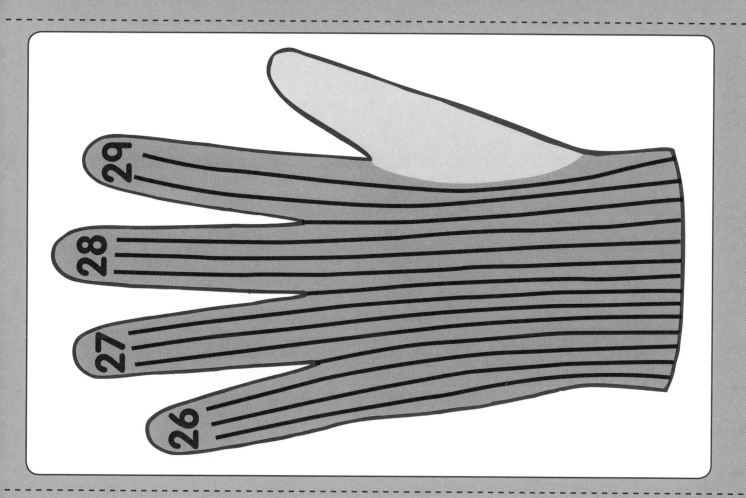

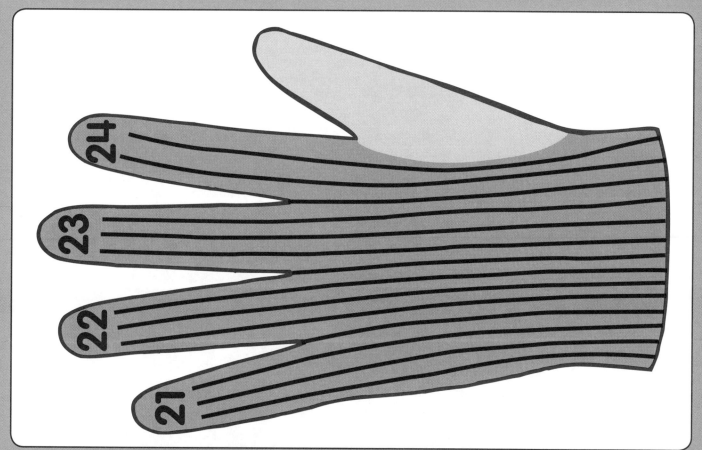

Math Centers—Take It to Your Seat • EMC 3020

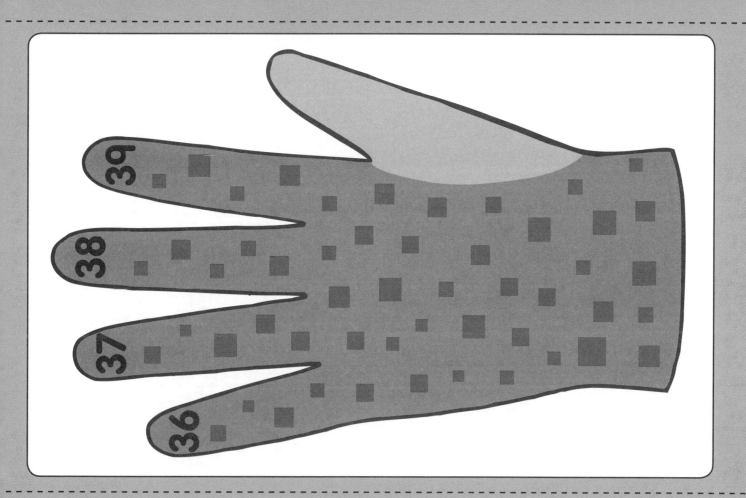

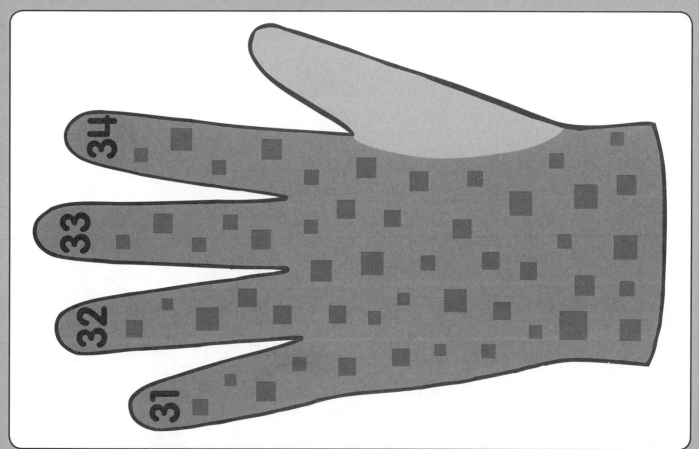

Math Centers—Take It to Your Seat • EMC 3020

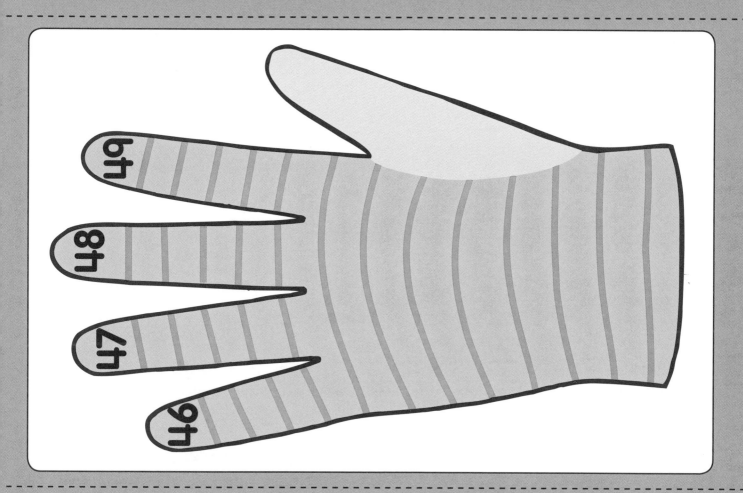

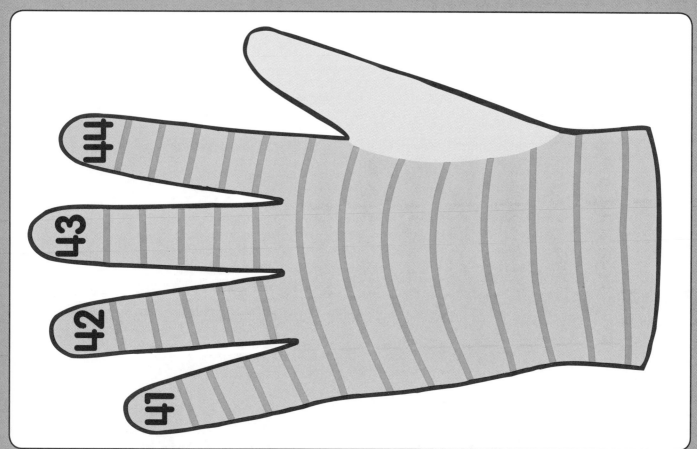

Thumb fronts

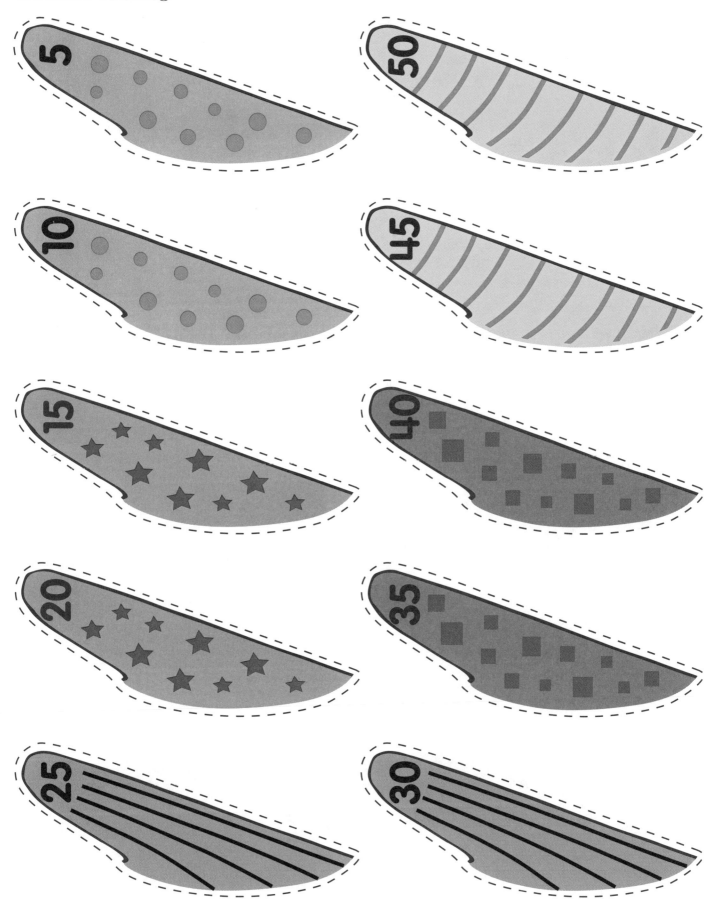

Thumb backs

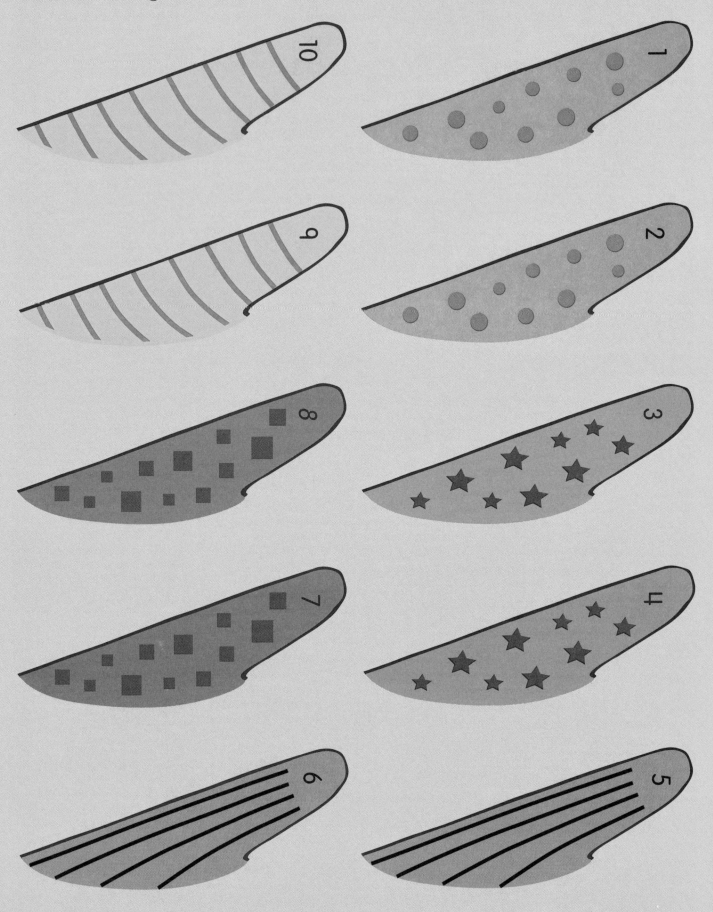

Record
Form

Name _____

Groovy Gloves

Copy the thumb numbers in order.

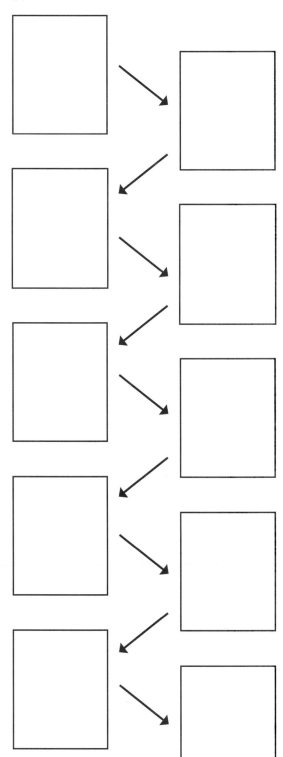

Record
Form

Name _____

Groovy Gloves

Copy the thumb numbers in order.

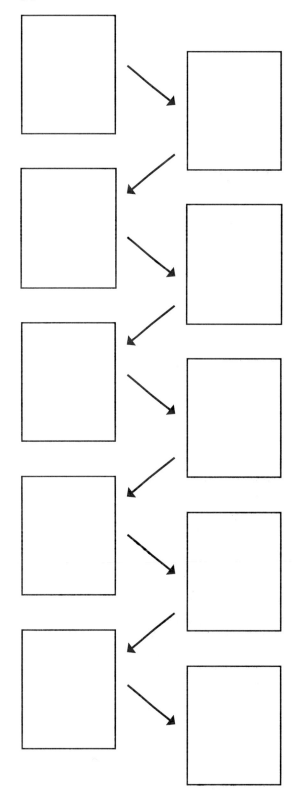

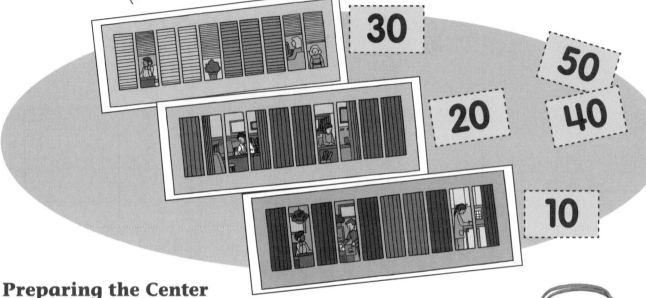

Stack a Skyscraper

Preparing the Center

1. Laminate and cut out the front illustration on page 107, the center challenge and label on page 109, and the skyscraper windows and number cards on pages 111–121.

2. Tape the illustration onto the front of the bag.

3. Tape the center challenge onto the back of the bag and the label onto the bottom of the bag.

4. Reproduce the student record form on page 123 for students.

5. Place the floors and windows in the bag.

Using the Center

Small-Group Practice

As a group, lay the rows of windows together to create a tall skyscraper. Start at the bottom and count the windows in that row. Beside the row, place the number card that tells how many windows you counted (10). Continue counting and placing numbers beside each row (20 through 100). Have students read the numbers beside the rows. Explain that they are counting sets of ten windows, and that is called counting by tens.

Independent Practice

The student builds the skyscraper by stacking rows of windows. Beginning at the bottom left, the student counts the windows and places a number card telling how many windows there are in all. The student copies the numbers onto the record form.

Self-Checking Key

Students flip the number cards. If the cards are in the correct order, they form a picture of a happy sunflower.

Stack a Skyscraper

Math Centers—Take It to Your Seat • EMC 3020

Stack a Skyscraper

Skill:
Counting by 10s

Stack a Skyscraper

1. Stack the rows of windows to make a skyscraper.

2. Start at the bottom. Count the windows in the first row.

3. At the end of the row, place the correct number card to tell how many windows there are.

4. Keep counting. Place a number card after each row.

5. Copy the number cards in order onto the record form.

Math Centers—Take It to Your Seat • EMC 3020

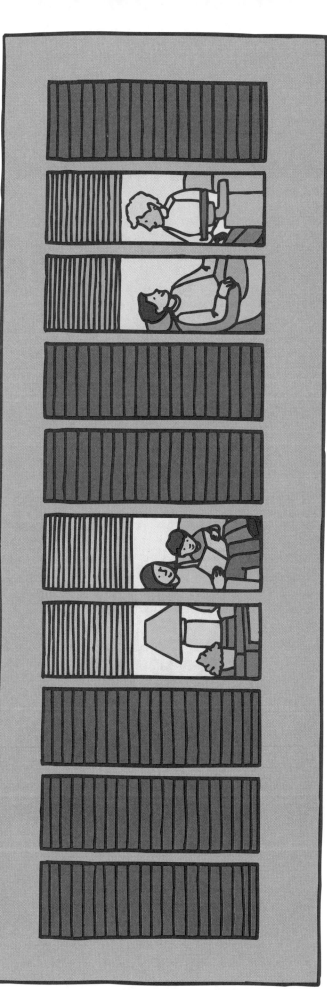

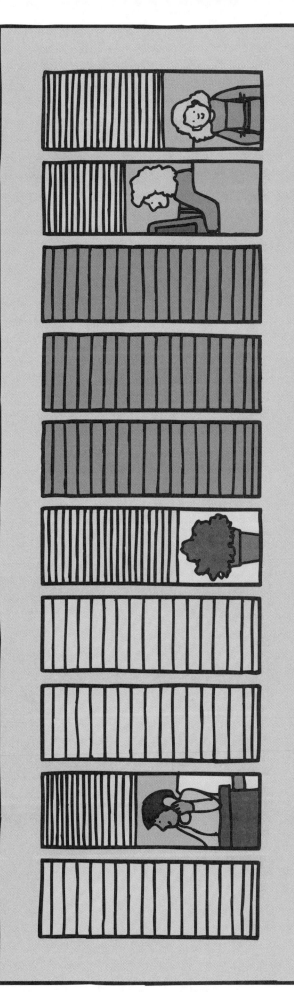
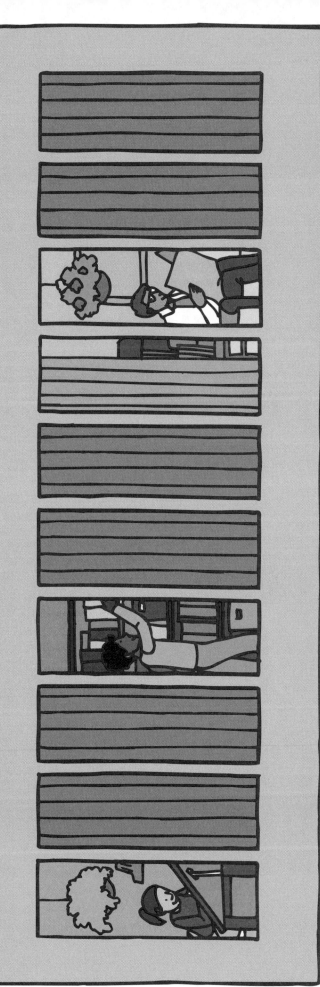

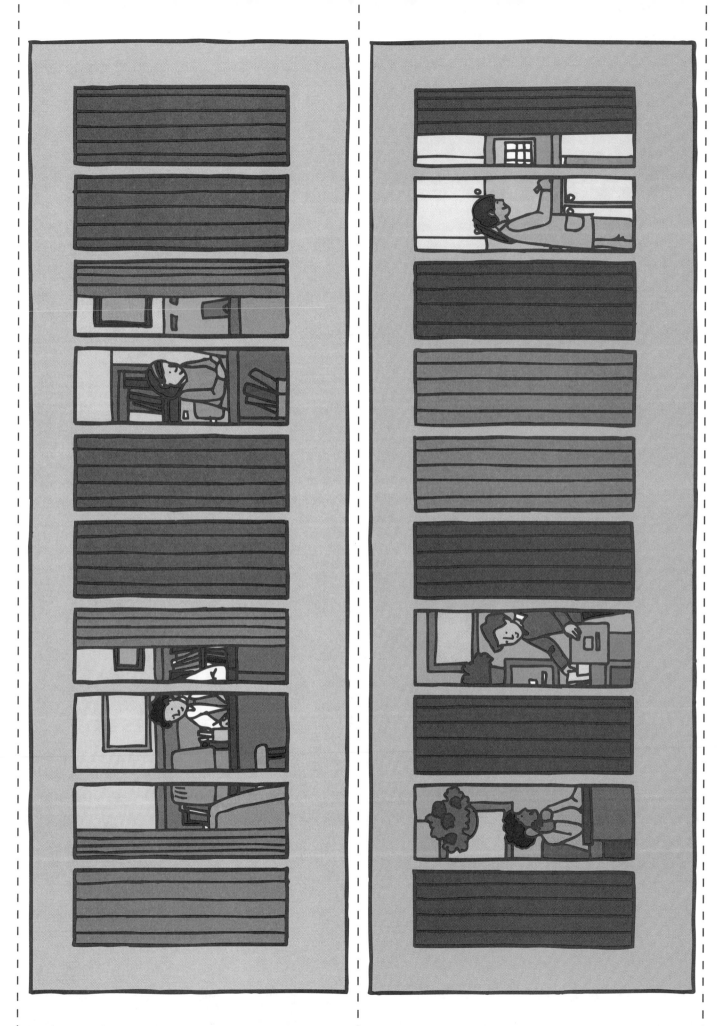

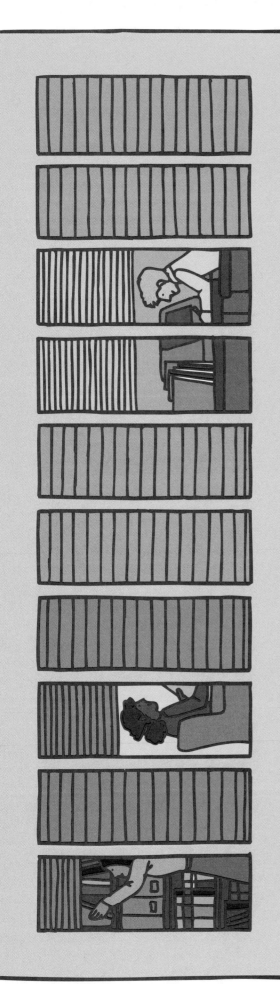

Math Centers—Take It to Your Seat • EMC 3020

100	50
90	40
80	30
70	20
60	10

Record
Form

Name _____

Stack a Skyscraper

Copy the numbers in order.

Name _____

Stack a Skyscraper

Copy the numbers in order.

The Sweet Shop

Preparing the Center

1. Laminate and cut out the front illustration on page 125, the center challenge and label on page 127, and the sweets cards and coin purses on pages 129–135.

2. Tape the illustration onto the front of the bag.

3. Tape the center challenge onto the back of the bag and the label onto the bottom of the bag.

4. Reproduce the student record form on page 137 for students.

5. Place the sweets cards and coin purses in the bag.

Using the Center

Small-Group Practice

Give each student a coin purse card. Have students count the money to determine the value of the coins on their cards. Draw a sweets card from the bag. The student with the purse whose value matches the value of the sweets card puts his or her card next to it. Match all the cards in the same manner.

Independent Practice

The student lines up the sweets cards on a flat surface. The student chooses a coin purse and counts the coins to determine its value. The student matches the purse to the sweet with the same value. The student then draws lines on the record form to show the correct matches.

Self-Checking Key

Students flip the sweets cards and coin purses. Correct matches will have the same colors.

The Sweet Shop

Math Centers—Take It to Your Seat • EMC 3020

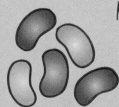

The Sweet Shop

Skills:
Money, Determining Value, Equivalent Numbers

The Sweet Shop

1. Choose a sweet.

2. Find the purse with the coins that match the price of the sweet.

3. Match all the sweets with purses.

4. Draw lines on the record form to show the correct matches.

Math Centers—Take It to Your Seat • EMC 3020

20¢

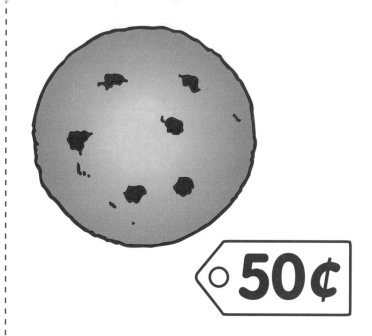

50¢

30¢

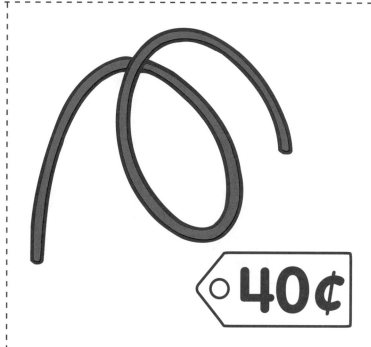

40¢

10¢

60¢

75¢

15¢

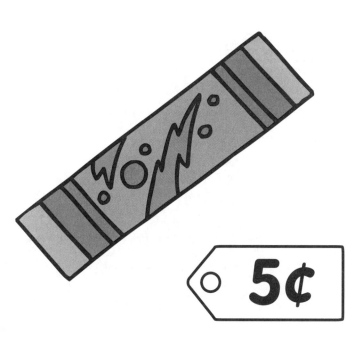

5¢

45¢

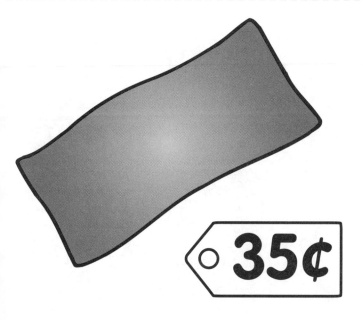

35¢

65¢

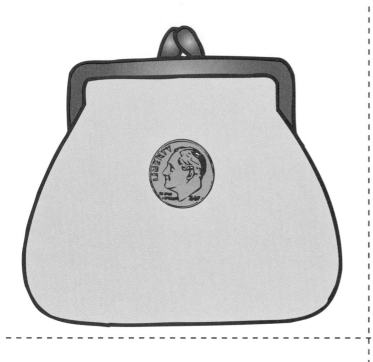

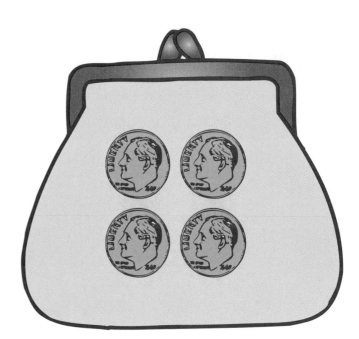

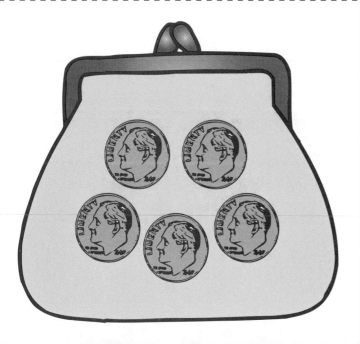

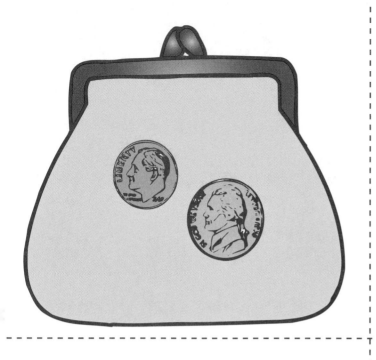

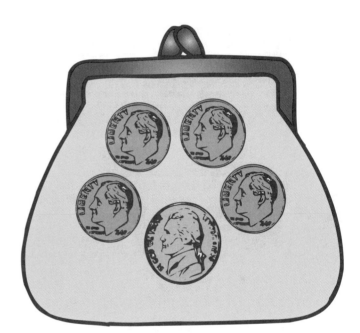

Name _____

The Sweet Shop

Draw a line to show the correct matches.

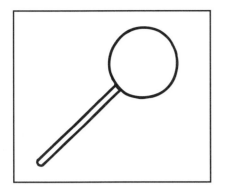

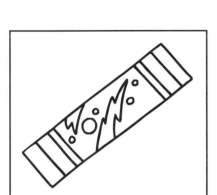

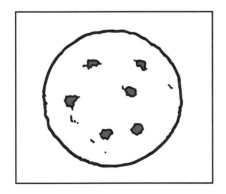

Hour by Hour

Preparing the Center

1. Laminate and cut out the front illustration on page 139, the center challenge and label on page 141, and the clockfaces on pages 143–147.

2. Tape the illustration onto the front of the bag.

3. Tape the center challenge onto the back of the bag and the label onto the bottom of the bag.

4. Reproduce the student record form on page 149 for students.

5. Place the clockfaces in the bag.

Using the Center

Small-Group Practice

Spread out the clockfaces on a flat surface. Ask the first student to choose the clockface that shows 1 o'clock. The student holds the clockface so that other students can see it. Have the next student choose the clockface that shows 2 o'clock. Continue with each clockface in order. Then read the faces by saying the times.

Independent Practice

The student finds the clockface that shows 1 o'clock. The student continues to find and place in order the clockfaces for each hour. The student draws the hour hand on the clocks on the record form to show the given time.

Self-Checking Key

Students flip the clockfaces after they are in order from left to right. At the bottom of the cards are tiny circles. The circles will be in order from 1 to 12 if the clockfaces are in the correct order.

Hour by Hour

Hour by Hour

Skills:
Number Order,
Reading Time to the Hour

Hour by Hour

1. Find the clockface that shows 1 o'clock.

2. Find the clockfaces for 2 o'clock, 3 o'clock, 4 o'clock, 5 o'clock, 6 o'clock, 7 o'clock, 8 o'clock, 9 o'clock, 10 o'clock, 11 o'clock, and 12 o'clock.

3. Place the clocks in a line.

4. Draw the hour hand on the clockfaces on the record form in the correct place.

Math Centers—Take It to Your Seat • EMC 3020

Hour by Hour

Draw the hour hand to show the correct time.

2 o'clock

5 o'clock

9 o'clock

3 o'clock

Sort by Shape

Preparing the Center

1. Laminate and cut out the front illustration on page 151, the center challenge and label on page 153, and the sorting mats and object cards on pages 155–161.

2. Tape the illustration onto the front of the bag.

3. Tape the center challenge onto the back of the bag and the label onto the bottom of the bag.

4. Reproduce the student record form on page 163 for students.

5. Place the sorting mats and object cards in the bag.

Using the Center

Small-Group Practice

Each student has a sorting mat. The object cards remain in the bag. Draw one object card from the bag. Students determine which sorting mat the object card should go on by determining its shape. Repeat until all objects are sorted.

Independent Practice

The student lays out the sorting mats. The student chooses an object card and places it on the correct mat. The student continues until all object cards are sorted. The student completes the record form by drawing one object for each geometric shape.

Self-Checking Key

Students flip the sorted object cards to see if the colors are the same.

Sort by Shape

Math Centers—Take It to Your Seat • EMC 3020

Sort by Shape

Skill:
Identifying and Matching Objects
Representing Geometric Shapes

Sort by Shape

1. Lay the sorting mats in a line.

2. Choose a card. Place it on the correct mat.

3. Sort all the cards onto the correct mats.

4. Draw one object for each shape on the record form.

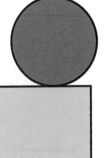

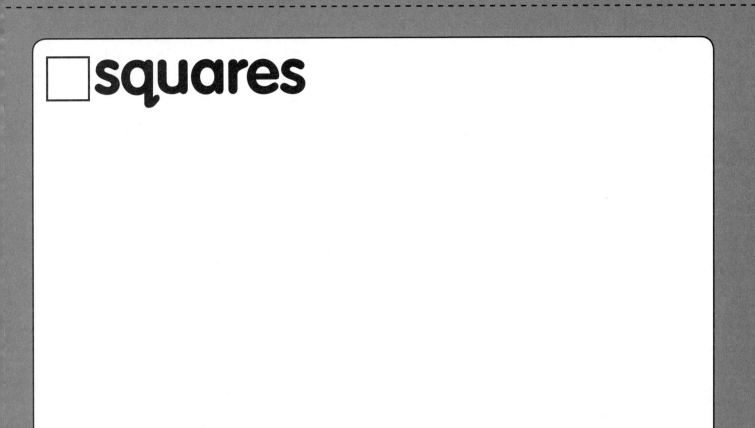

□ squares

□ rectangles

 **circles**

 **triangles**

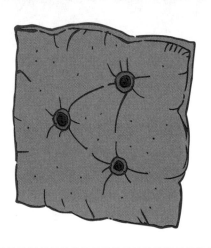

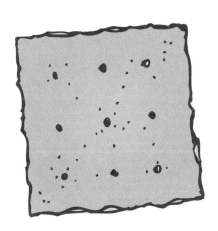

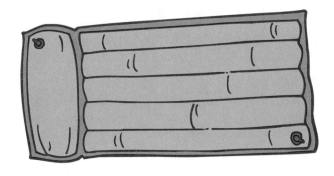

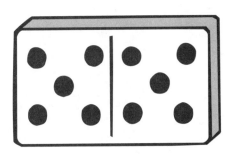

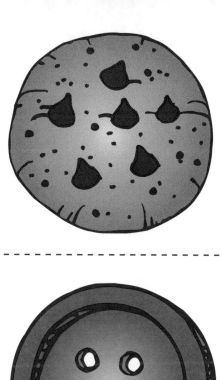

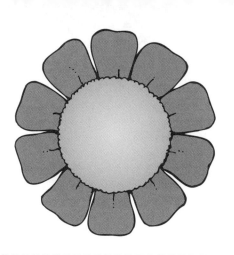

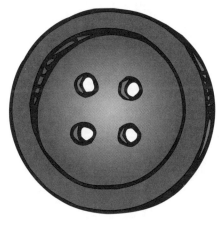

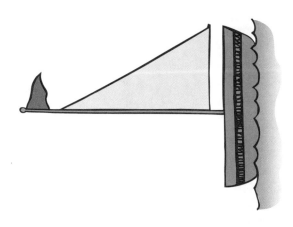

Sort by Shape

Draw each shape.

square	**circle**
triangle	**rectangle**

Caterpillar Patterns

Preparing the Center

1. Laminate and cut out the front illustration on page 165, the center challenge and label on page 167, and the caterpillar mats and segment shapes on pages 169–175.

2. Tape the illustration onto the front of the bag.

3. Tape the center challenge onto the back of the bag and the label onto the bottom of the bag.

4. Reproduce the student record form on page 177 for students.

5. Place the caterpillar mats and segment shapes in the bag.

Using the Center

Small-Group Practice

As a group, choose a caterpillar mat. Read the pattern on the mat. Choose colored segments to make a pattern of that type on the mat. Have each student choose a different mat and make the designated pattern. Finally, have students color their caterpillar pattern on the record form and write the pattern name.

Independent Practice

The student chooses a caterpillar mat. The student reads the pattern name. The student creates a caterpillar with that pattern. The student colors the caterpillar pattern on the record form and writes its pattern name.

Self-Checking Key

Students write a color key for the pattern name on their record forms. Then they read the pattern using color names.

A–red
B–yellow   red yellow red yellow red yellow

Caterpillar Patterns

Caterpillar Patterns

Skills:
Making Patterns,
Naming Patterns

Caterpillar Patterns

1. Take a caterpillar mat.

2. Read the pattern.

3. Choose colored shapes to make the pattern.

4. Color the caterpillar on the record form to match your caterpillar.

5. Write the pattern name on the record form.

Math Centers—Take It to Your Seat • EMC 3020

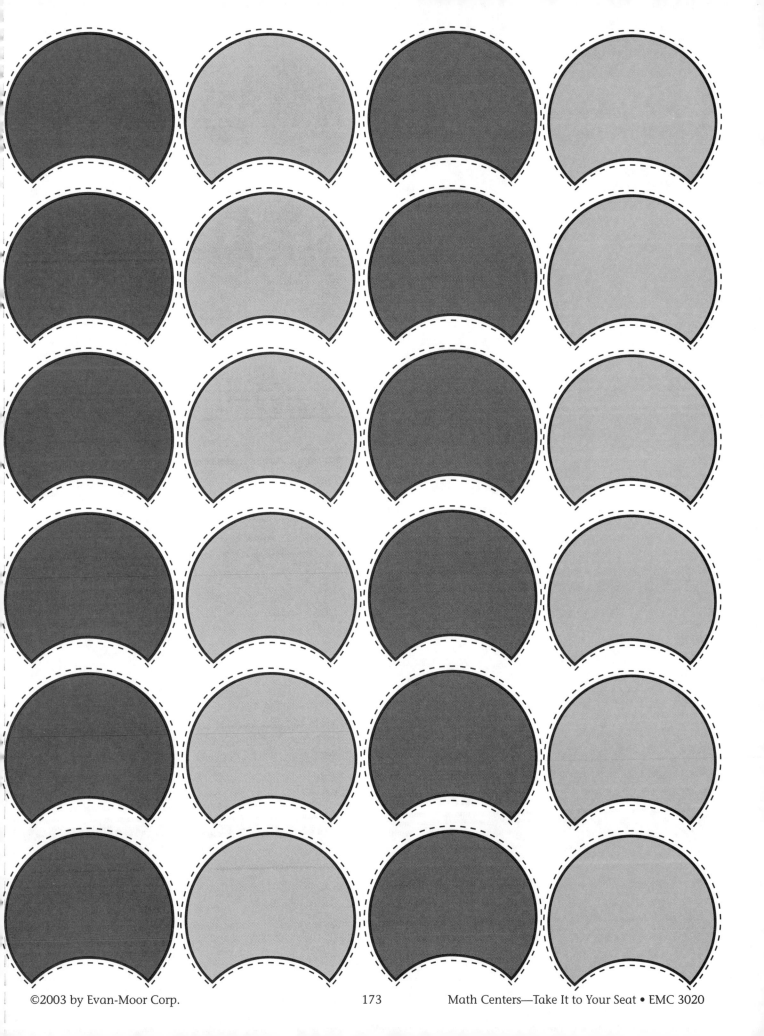

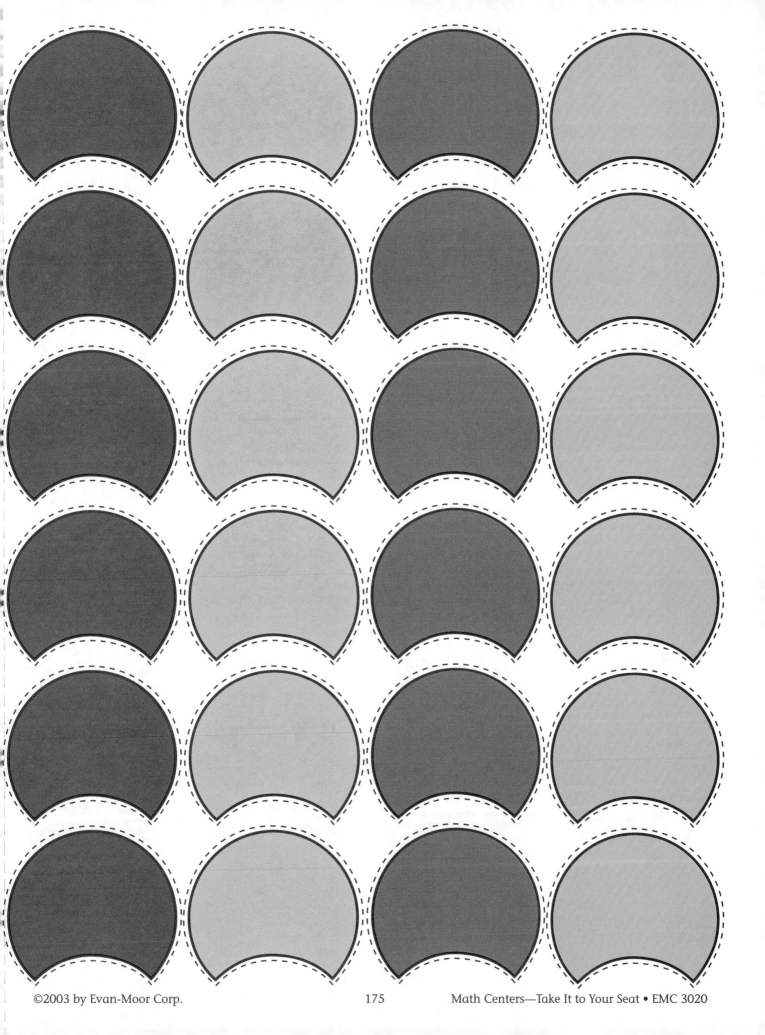

Math Centers—Take It to Your Seat • EMC 3020

Math Centers—Take It to Your Seat • EMC 3020

Name _____

Caterpillar Patterns

Color the caterpillar to match the one you made.
Write the name of your pattern.

Record
Form

My pattern is: _____

- -

Name _____

Caterpillar Patterns

Color the caterpillar to match the one you made.
Write the name of your pattern.

Record
Form

My pattern is: _____

Sea Stars

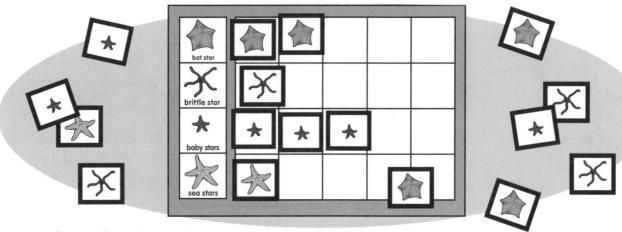

Preparing the Center

1. Laminate and cut out the front illustration on page 179, the center challenge and label on page 181, and the graphing mats and sea star cards on pages 183–191. Place each set of cards in an envelope. Label the envelopes *Orange Set, Purple Set, Yellow Set,* and *Green Set.*

2. Tape the illustration onto the front of the bag.

3. Tape the center challenge onto the back of the bag and the label onto the bottom of the bag.

4. Reproduce the student record form on the inside back cover for students.

5. Place the sorting mats and the sea star cards in the bag.

Using the Center

Small-Group Practice

As a group, create a graph using the graphing mat and the sea star cards. Place one set of cards in the bag. Students take turns reaching into the bag and removing a card. Then they place the sea star in the correct row on the graphing mat. When all the sea stars have been placed, count how many are in each row. Record the numbers on the record form.

Independent Practice

The student chooses a sea star and places it on the graphing mat in the correct row. Then the student counts the number of sea stars in each row and records the numbers on the record form. Finally, the student colors one square for each sea star on the graph.

Self-Checking Key

Students flip over the sea stars in each row to see if the colors match. When the sea stars are flipped over, the graphing mat should match the graph on the student record form.

Sea Stars

Math Centers—Take It to Your Seat • EMC 3020

Sea Stars

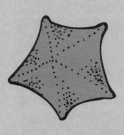

Skills:
Graphing, Counting

Sea Stars

1. Take a sea star card.

2. Place the sea star on the graph in the correct row.

3. Repeat with each sea star.

4. Write the numbers on the record form.

5. Color the graph on the record form to match your graph.

 Math Centers—Take It to Your Seat • EMC 3020

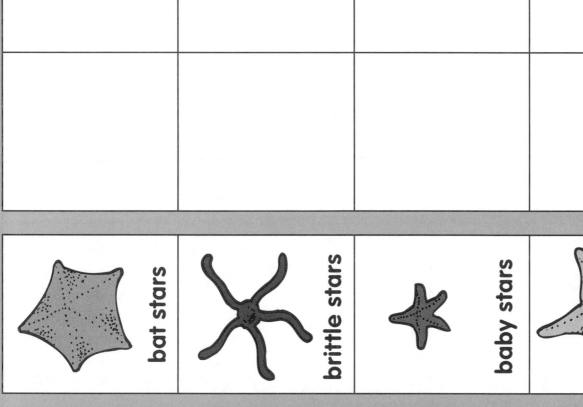

bat stars

brittle stars

baby stars

sea stars

Math Centers—Take It to Your Seat • EMC 3020

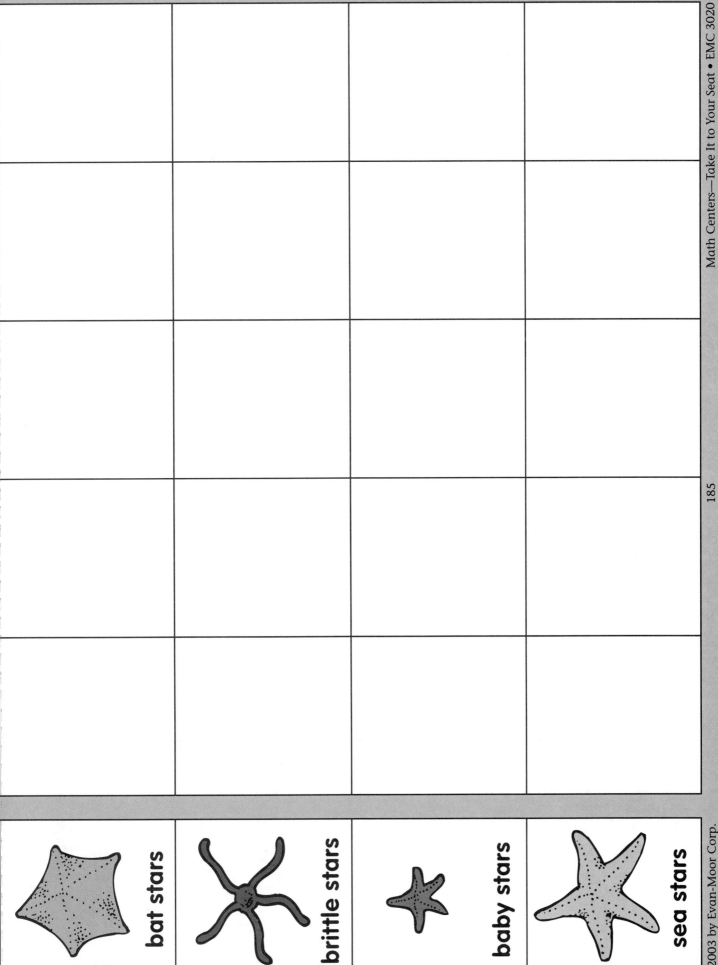

bat stars

brittle stars

baby stars

sea stars

Math Centers—Take It to Your Seat • EMC 3020

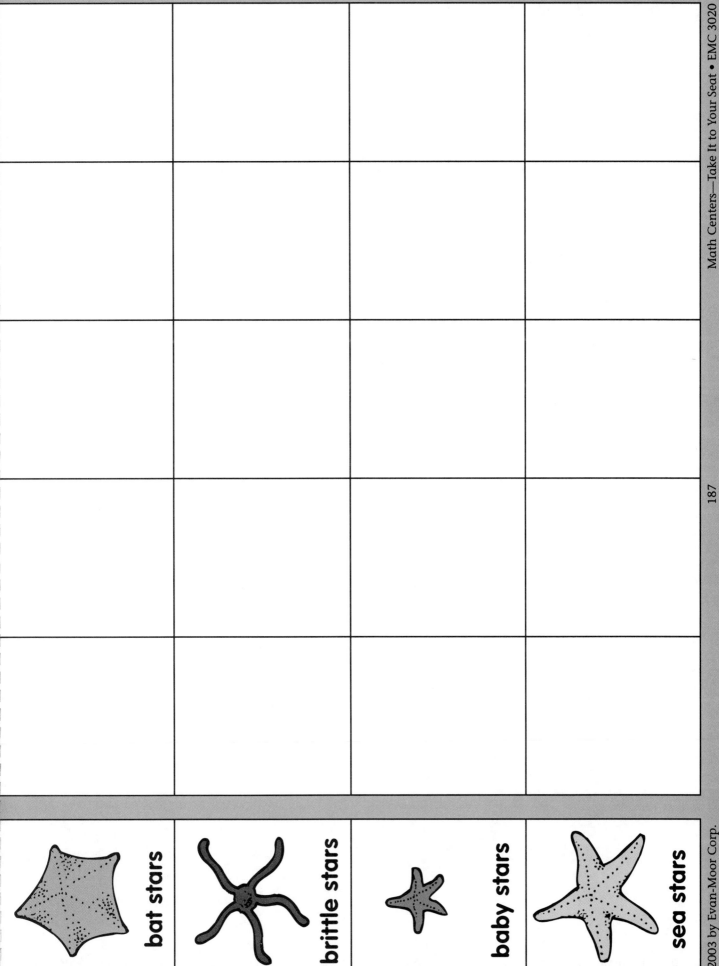

bat stars

brittle stars

baby stars

sea stars

Math Centers—Take It to Your Seat • EMC 3020

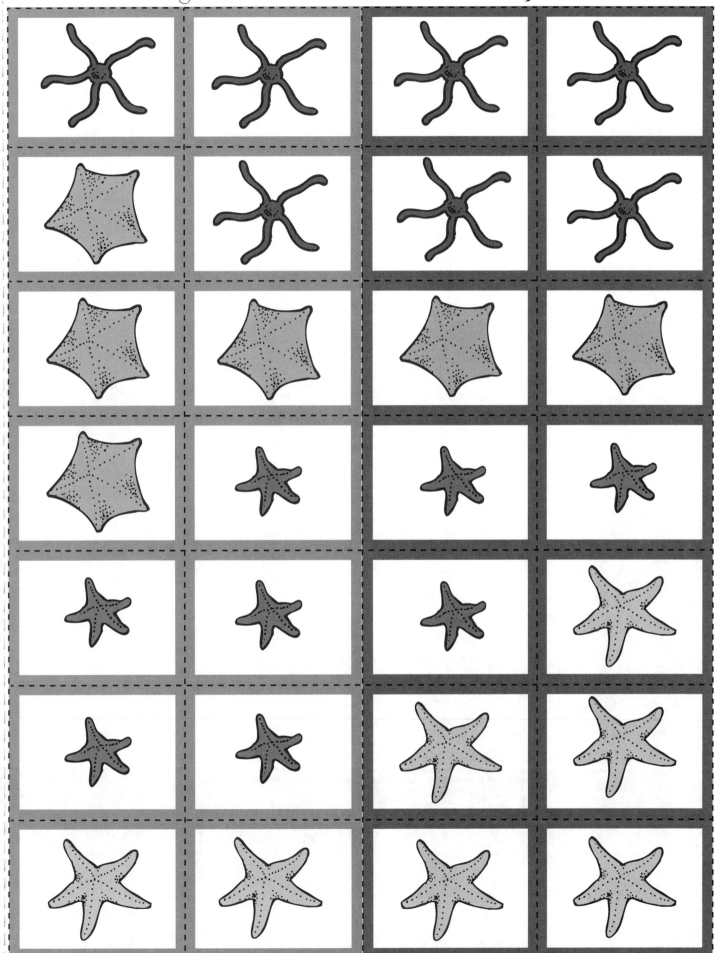

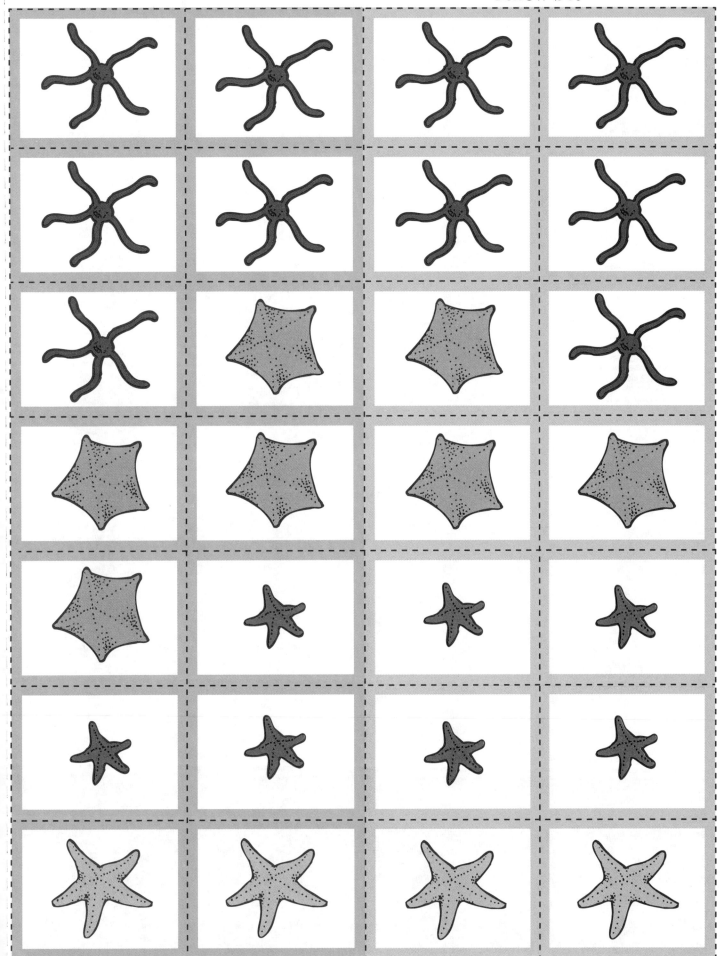